Sno... ...g

by Ji... ...owell

CHAPTER ONE
A decision

It was dark when Dad got home.

"How did you get on?" Mum asked.

"Two climbers got lost in the fog," Dad said. "Nina found them."

Ruth gave Nina a big hug.

"You're the best search and rescue dog ever, Nina!" she said.

"Nina *was* the best search and rescue dog," Dad said. "But she is not as quick as she was. I think it's time for Nina to stop working. It's time to let a young dog take over."

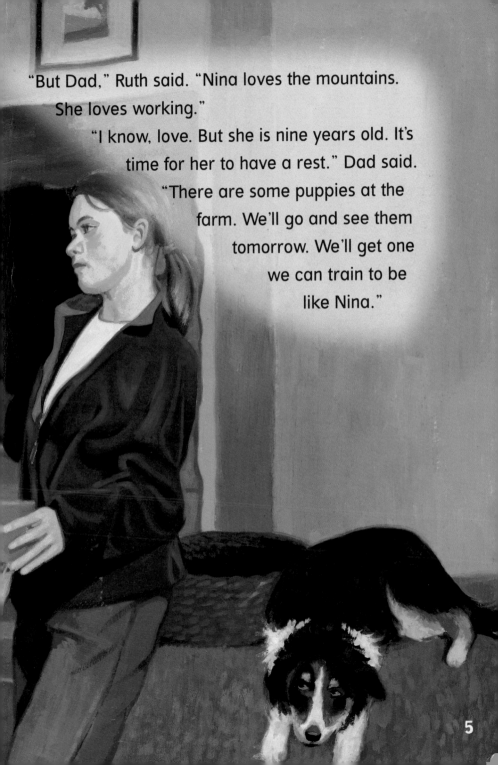

"But Dad," Ruth said. "Nina loves the mountains. She loves working."

"I know, love. But she is nine years old. It's time for her to have a rest." Dad said. "There are some puppies at the farm. We'll go and see them tomorrow. We'll get one we can train to be like Nina."

CHAPTER TWO

A new puppy

Ruth and Dad went to see the puppies. "This one looks a bright little thing," Dad said.

The puppy was a sheepdog. It was black and white. It had a big black spot over one eye. "He looks just like Nina when she was a puppy," Ruth said.

"What shall we call him, Ruth?" Dad said.

They were on their way home in the car.

"How about Ben?" Ruth said.

Ruth cuddled Ben. He was very cute. But she still felt sad when they got home. Nina was sitting by the gate. Ruth knew how much Nina loved working. She would not want to give it up.

CHAPTER THREE

A good nose

Ben started his training. He was a quick learner.
He loved the hide and seek games that were part
of his training.

Dad took Ben
out most days.
The puppy had
to get used to the
sheep on the hills.
He also had to get
used to searching for a
scent. He had a good
nose. But sometimes he ran
after a bird or a hare instead.
Ben had a lot to learn before
he could be a trainee
search and rescue dog.

Ruth went with Dad and Ben on training weekends.
She had to hide and see if Ben could find her.
One day he would have to do this for real.
He would have to find lost climbers or
walkers on the mountains.

Nina had made friends with Ben. Dad and Ruth took them for walks together every day. But Nina just sat at the gate when Ben went off for his training. Her big brown eyes looked sad.

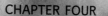

CHAPTER FOUR
Call-out!

Ben was now two years old. He was used to working on the mountain. He had trained at night, and in snow. Now he was getting used to working with an RAF helicopter. Soon Ben would be ready for his first call-out.

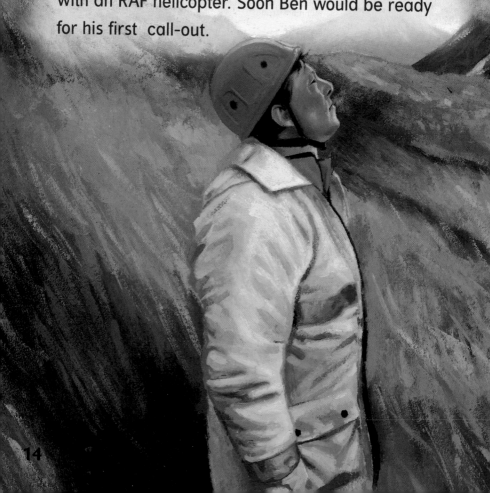

Ben's first call-out came. It was a dark day in December. It had been snowing hard for two days. Mum, Dad and Ruth were just sitting down to eat their lunch when the call-out came.

Some snowboarders were up on the mountain. They were in trouble.

"OK, Ben," Dad said. "This is it!"

Ruth patted Nina. She was sitting at the back door, wagging her tail. She wanted to go, too.

"No, Nina. Stay with Ruth," Dad said.

CHAPTER FIVE
A find

"The snowboarders are up on Bell's Peak," Dad
said. "We can take the jeep up the track. Then we
can walk from there."
A man called Simon and his dog, Tip, were also on
the call-out. There was a doctor too – in case one of
the snowboarders was hurt.

It was still snowing hard.

"I don't like the way this snow is building up,"
Dad said. "This is avalanche snow."

They stopped the jeep at the end of the track. They stepped out into the thick white snow. Ben had a bright yellow coat that made him easy to see. He also had a bell on his collar.

Dad gave the signal to search.
The dogs ran backwards and
forwards over the snow.
They were searching
for a scent.

At last there was a
bark. Ben had
found something.

CHAPTER SIX
Avalanche!

Ben had found three snowboarders. But one was still missing. She had been swept downhill. The search had to go on. Ben and Tip ran backwards and forwards over the snow.

But it was getting dark, and there was bad news to come. There had been an avalanche. The snowboarder could be buried in the snow.

"We are running out of time," Dad said. "We need …" Suddenly, he stopped talking. He peered through the snow. It was Nina – coming up the track towards them!

CHAPTER SEVEN
Nina to the rescue

"Nina!" Dad called. He patted her. Then he gave
the signal to search.
Nina ran backwards and forwards over the snow.
Her ears were up as she listened for a sound. Her
nose was down as she searched for a scent. No dog
had a better nose than Nina.

Nina went on down the mountain. She was almost
out of sight. Then Dad heard her bark. He ran
towards her. Nina had her nose in the snow and
she was digging. She had found the missing
snowboarder.

CHAPTER EIGHT

Nina's reward

The next day, Nina's picture was in the paper.
There was also a picture of the snowboarder she
had rescued. The snowboarder had been buried
under a metre of snow. The report said that Nina
had saved her life.

A reporter rang Dad to ask about the rescue.
"Nina got out of the house. Then somehow she got
out of the garden," he said. "She seemed to know
she was needed."

Ruth patted Nina. She knew how Nina had got out of the garden.

"We showed them, Nina!" she said.

"You are still the best search and rescue dog ever!"